Sirtfood diet cookbook for beginners

A smart and simple recipe can start a new way of cooking. Start your journey with amazing recipes and start to lower blood pressure, lose weight fast and reset your metabolism

SOPHIE GARDNER

Sommario

INTRODUCTION

Theoretically, this slimming diet is sold to make you lose weight quickly and without depriving yourself. It appeared for the first time in 2016 in a book soberly entitled The Sirtfood diet and written by two English graduates in nutritional medicine, Aidan Goggins and then Glen Matten.

In practice, this involves consuming "superfoods" that are sirtuins rich, belonging to a family of enzymes with seven members, for example, SIRT1, SIRT2, up to SIRT7. According to the authors, these enzymes with multiple benefits boost the immune system; it protects against neurodegenerative diseases and can act against cell aging.

Among the foods that would contain these famous enzymes are apples, blueberries, coffee, matcha tea, turmeric, dates, celery, onion, citrus, olive oil, arugula, soy, but also dark chocolate and red wine!

The Sirtuin Diet (in the original Sirtfood Diet) is based on proteins. But she still has nothing in common with Low-Carb, Paleo & Co. Because, as the name suggests, the focus is on an exceptional protein - the enzyme Sirtuin. Anyone who has thought directly of animal products when it comes to proteins is wrong.

They are plant foods that stimulate the formation of the enzyme and form the nutritional form's basic idea. A new era of superfoods. And something else distinguishes the trend from all the others: long-term calories do not have to be counted, nor are certain foods prohibited.

The idea: inclusion instead of exclusion

The diet was developed by the British nutritionists Aidan Goggins and Glen Matten. Their theory: The enzyme that is particularly active in lean of people and fat loss. This can be stimulated by eating certain foods.

Sirtuins are also released during fasting, but the inventors wanted to avoid the negative side effects of a strict fasting cure.

Kick start for the metabolism

In the beginning, a 2-phase diet is recommended to fuel the metabolism and the sirtuins. One thousand calories are consumed in the first three days. After that, the intake is increased to 1500 calories. Here you stick to green juices and sirtuin-based meals.

After seven days you eat again as needed, of course still a potpourri of sirt foods. These phases are not a must! Even if you "only" integrate the sirt foods and live healthily, you will see success.

SIRTFOOD BREAKFAST

Apricot Oatmeal Cookies

Preparation Time: 30 minutes

Cooking Time: 10 minutes

Servings: 4

Ingredients:

- 1/2 cup (1 stick) butter, softened
- 2/3 cup light brown sugar packed
- 1 egg
- 3/4 cup all-purpose flour
- 1/2 tsp baking soda
- 1/2 tsp vanilla infusion
- 1/2 tsp cinnamon
- 1/4 tsp salt
- 1 teaspoon 1/2 cups chopped oats
- 3/4 cup yolks
- 1/4 cup sliced apricots
- 1/3 cup slivered almonds

Directions:

1. Preheat oven to 350°.
2. In a big bowl, combine with the butter, sugar, and egg until smooth.

3. In another bowl, whisk the flour, baking soda, cinnamon, and salt together.

4. Stir the dry ingredients to the butter-sugar bowl.

5. Now stir in the oats, raisins, apricots, and almonds.

Nutrition: Calories 82 Fat 2g Carbohydrates 12g Protein 1g

Sirt Energy Balls

Preparation Time: 30 minutes

Cooking Time: 0 minute

Servings: 20

Ingredients:

- 1 mug of mixed nuts (with plenty of walnuts)

- 7 Medjool dates

- 1 tablespoon of coconut oil

- 2 tablespoons of cocoa powder

- Zest of 1 orange (optional)

Directions:

1. Start by placing the nuts in a food processor and grind them until almost powdered (more or less depending on the preferred texture of your energy balls).

2. Add the Medjool dates, coconut oil, cacao powder, and run the blender again until fully mixed. Place the blend in a refrigerator for half an hour, and then shape them into balls. You can add in the zest of an orange as you blend.

Nutrition: Calories 261 Fat 6g Carbohydrates 41g Protein 4g

Chicken Rolls with Pesto

Preparation Time: 10 Minutes

Cooking Time: 0 Minute

Servings: 2

Ingredients:

- 2 tablespoon Pine nuts
- 25 g Yeast flakes
- 1 clove Garlic (chopped)
- 15 g fresh basil
- 85 ml Olive oil
- 2 pieces Chicken breast

Directions:

1. Preheat the oven to 175 ° C.
2. Roast the pine nuts in a dry pan over medium heat for 3 minutes until golden brown. Place on a plate and set aside.
3. Put the pine nuts, yeast flakes and garlic in a food processor and grind them finely.
4. Add the basil and oil and mix briefly until you get a pesto.

5. Season with salt and pepper.

6. Place each piece of chicken breast between 2 pieces of cling film

7. Beat with a saucepan or rolling pin until the chicken breast is about 0.6 cm thick.

8. Remove the cling film and spread the pesto on the chicken.

9. Roll up the chicken breasts and use cocktail skewers to hold them together.

10. Season with salt and pepper.

11. Melt the coconut oil in a pan and brown the chicken rolls on all sides over high heat.

12. Put the chicken rolls in a baking dish, place in the oven and bake for 15-20 minutes until they are done.

13. Slice the rolls diagonally and serve with the rest of the pesto.

14. Goes well with a tomato salad.

Nutrition: Calories: 345.4 Fat: 14.5 g Cholesterol: 44.1 mg Sodium: 419.5 mg Potassium: 84.1 mg Total Carbohydrate: 44.1 g Protein: 9.0 g

Fried Cauliflower Rice

Preparation Time: 30 Minutes

Cooking Time: 15 Minutes

Servings: 2

Ingredients:

- 1 piece Cauliflower
- 2 tablespoon Coconut oil
- 1 piece Red onion
- 4 cloves Garlic
- 60 ml Vegetable broth
- 1.5 cm fresh ginger
- 1 teaspoon Chili flakes
- 1/2 pieces Carrot
- 1/2 pieces Red bell pepper
- 1/2 pieces Lemon (the juice)
- 2 tablespoon Pumpkin seeds
- 2 tablespoon fresh coriander

Directions:

1. Cut the cauliflower into small rice grains in a food processor.

2. Finely chop the onion, garlic and ginger, cut the carrot into thin strips, dice the bell pepper and finely chop the herbs.

3. Melt 1 tablespoon of coconut oil in a pan and add half of the onion and garlic to the pan and fry briefly until translucent.

4. Add cauliflower rice and season with salt.

5. Pour in the broth and stir everything until it evaporates and the cauliflower rice is tender.

6. Take the rice out of the pan and set it aside.

7. Melt the rest of the coconut oil in the pan and add the remaining onions, garlic, ginger, carrots and peppers.

8. Fry for a few minutes until the vegetables are tender. Season them with a little salt.

9. Add the cauliflower rice again, heat the whole dish and add the lemon juice.

10. Garnish with pumpkin seeds and coriander before serving.

Nutrition: Calories: 129.1 Fat: 5.3g Cholesterol: 93mg Sodium: 768mg Potassium: 639mg Carbohydrates: 14.7g Protein: 8.5g

Kale & Mushroom Frittata

Preparation Time: 15 Minutes

Cooking Time: 30 Minutes

Servings: 5

Ingredients:

- 8 eggs
- ½ cup unsweetened almond milk
- Salt and ground black pepper, to taste
- 1 tablespoon olive oil
- 1 onion, chopped
- 1 garlic clove, minced
- 1 cup fresh mushrooms, chopped
- 1½ cups fresh kale, tough ribs removed and chopped

Directions:

1. Preheat oven to 350°F.
2. In a large bowl, place the eggs, coconut milk, salt, and black pepper, and beat well. Set aside.
3. In a large ovenproof wok, heat the oil over medium heat and sauté the onion and garlic for about 3–4 minutes.
4. Add the squash, kale, bell pepper, salt, and black pepper, and cook for about 8–10 minutes.

5. Stir in the mushrooms and cook for about 3–4 minutes.

6. Add the kale and cook for about 5 minutes.

7. Place the egg mixture on top evenly and cook for about 4 minutes, without stirring.

8. Transfer the wok in the oven and bake for about 12–15 minutes or until desired doneness.

9. Remove from the oven and place the frittata side for about 3–5 minutes before serving.

10. Cut into desired sized wedges and serve.

Nutrition: Calories 151 Total Fat 10.2 g Saturated Fat 2.6 g Cholesterol 262 mg Sodium 158 mg Total Carbs 5.6 g Fiber 1 g Sugar 1.7 g Protein 10.3 g

Kale, Apple, & Cranberry Salad

Preparation Time: 15 Minutes

Cooking Time: 0 Minute

Servings: 4

Ingredients:

- 6 cups fresh baby kale
- 3 large apples, cored and sliced
- ¼ cup unsweetened dried cranberries
- ¼ cup almonds, sliced
- 2 tablespoons extra-virgin olive oil
- 1 tablespoon raw honey
- Salt and ground black pepper, to taste

Directions:

1. In a salad bowl, place all the ingredients and toss to coat well.
2. Serve immediately.

Nutrition: Calories 253 Total Fat 10.3 g Saturated Fat 1.2 g Cholesterol 0 mg Sodium 84 mg Total Carbs 40.7 g Fiber 6.6 g Sugar 22.7 g Protein 4.7 g

Arugula, Strawberry, & Orange Salad

Preparation Time: 15 Minutes

Cooking Time: 0 Minute

Servings: 4

Ingredients:

- For Salad
- 6 cups fresh baby arugula
- 1½ cups fresh strawberries, hulled and sliced
- 2 oranges, peeled and segmented
- For Dressing
- 2 tablespoons fresh lemon juice
- 1 tablespoon raw honey
- 2 teaspoons extra-virgin olive oil
- 1 teaspoon Dijon mustard
- Salt and ground black pepper, to taste

Directions:

1. For salad: in a salad bowl, place all ingredients and mix.
2. For dressing: place all ingredients in another bowl and beat until well combined.
3. Place dressing on top of salad and toss to coat well.
4. Serve immediately.

Nutrition: Calories 107 Total Fat 2.9 g Saturated Fat 0.4 g Cholesterol 0 mg Sodium 63 mg Total Carbs 20.6 g Fiber 3.9 g Sugar 16.4 g Protein 2.1 g

Beef & Kale Salad

Preparation Time: 15 Minutes

Cooking Time: 8 Minutes

Servings: 2

Ingredients:

- For Steak
- 2 teaspoons olive oil
- 2 (4-ounce) strip steaks
- Salt and ground black pepper, to taste
- For Salad
- ¼ cup carrot, peeled and shredded
- ¼ cup cucumber, peeled, seeded, and sliced
- ¼ cup radish, sliced
- ¼ cup cherry tomatoes, halved
- 3 cups fresh kale, tough ribs removed and chopped
- For Dressing
- 1 tablespoon extra-virgin olive oil
- 1 tablespoon fresh lemon juice
- Salt and ground black pepper, to taste

Directions:

1. For steak: in a large heavy-bottomed wok, heat the oil over high heat and cook the steaks with salt and black pepper for about 3–4 minutes per side.
2. Transfer the steaks onto a cutting board for about 5 minutes before slicing.
3. For salad: place all ingredients in a salad bowl and mix.
4. For dressing: place all ingredients in another bowl and beat until well combined.
5. Cut the steaks into desired sized slices against the grain.
6. Place the salad onto each serving plate.
7. Top each plate with steak slices.
8. Drizzle with dressing and serve.

Nutrition: Calories 262 Total Fat 12 g Saturated Fat 1.6 g Cholesterol 63 mg Sodium 506 mg Total Carbs 15.2 g Fiber 2.5g Sugar 3.3 g Protein 25.2 g

Salmon Burgers

Preparation Time: 20 Minutes

Cooking Time: 15 Minutes

Servings: 5

Ingredients:

- For Burgers
- 1 teaspoon olive oil
- 1 cup fresh kale, tough ribs removed and chopped
- 1/3 cup shallots, chopped finely
- Salt and ground black pepper, to taste
- 16 ounces skinless salmon fillets
- ¾ cup cooked quinoa
- 2 tablespoons Dijon mustard
- 1 large egg, beaten
- For Salad
- 2½ tablespoons olive oil
- 2½ tablespoons red wine vinegar
- Salt and ground black pepper, to taste
- 8 cups fresh baby arugula
- 2 cups cherry tomatoes, halved

Directions:

1. For burgers: in a large non-stick wok, heat the oil over medium heat and sauté the kale, shallots, salt, and black pepper for about 4–5 minutes.
2. Remove from heat and transfer the kale mixture into a large bowl.
3. Set aside to cool slightly.
4. With a knife, chop 4 ounces of salmon and transfer into the bowl of kale mixture.
5. In a food processor, add the remaining salmon and pulse until finely chopped.
6. Transfer the finely chopped salmon into the bowl of kale mixture.
7. Then, add remaining ingredients and stir until fully combined.
8. Make 5 equal-sized patties from the mixture.
9. Heat a lightly greased large non-stick wok over medium heat and cook the patties for about 4–5 minutes per side.
10. For dressing: in a glass bowl, add the oil, vinegar, shallots, salt, and black pepper, and beat until well combined.
11. Add arugula and tomatoes and toss to coat well.

12. Divide the salad onto on serving plates and top each with 1 patty.

13. Serve immediately.

Nutrition: Calories 329 Total Fat 15.8 g Saturated Fat 2.4 g Cholesterol 77 mg Sodium 177 mg Total Carbs 24 g Fiber 3.6 g Sugar 2.7 g Protein 24.9 g

Chicken with Broccoli & Mushrooms

Preparation Time: 15 Minutes

Cooking Time: 25 Minutes

Servings: 6

Ingredients:

- 3 tablespoons olive oil
- 1 pound skinless, boneless chicken breast, cubed
- 1 medium onion, chopped
- 6 garlic cloves, minced
- 2 cups fresh mushrooms, sliced
- 16 ounces small broccoli florets
- ¼ cup water
- Salt and ground black pepper, to taste

Directions:

1. Heat the oil in a large wok over medium heat and cook the chicken cubes for about 4–5 minutes.
2. With a slotted spoon, transfer the chicken cubes onto a plate.
3. In the same wok, add the onion and sauté for about 4–5 minutes.
4. Add the mushrooms and cook for about 4–5 minutes.

5. Stir in the cooked chicken, broccoli, and water, and cook (covered) for about 8–10 minutes, stirring occasionally.

6. Stir in salt and black pepper and remove from heat.

7. Serve hot.

Nutrition: Calories 197 Total Fat 10.1 g Saturated Fat 2 g Cholesterol 44 mg Sodium 82 mg Total Carbs 8.5 g Fiber 2.7 g Sugar 2.5 g Protein 20.1 g

Beef with Kale & Carrot

Preparation Time: 15 Minutes

Cooking Time: 12 Minutes

Servings: 4

Ingredients:

- 2 tablespoons coconut oil

- 4 garlic cloves, minced

- 1 pound beef sirloin steak, cut into bite-sized pieces

- Ground black pepper, to taste

- 1½ cups carrots, peeled and cut into matchsticks

- 1½ cups fresh kale, tough ribs removed and chopped

- 3 tablespoons tamari

Directions:

1. Melt the coconut oil in a wok over medium heat and sauté the garlic for about 1 minute.

2. Add the beef and black pepper and stir to combine.

3. Increase the heat to medium-high and cook for about 3–4 minutes or until browned from all sides.

4. Add the carrot, kale, and tamari, and cook for about 4–5 minutes.

5. Remove from the heat and serve hot.

Nutrition: Calories 311 Total Fat 13.8 g Saturated Fat 8.6 g Cholesterol 101 mg Sodium 700 mg Fiber 1.6 g Sugar 2.3 g Protein 37.1 g

SIRTFOOD LUNCH

Buckwheat Tabbouleh with Strawberries

Preparation Time: 10 minutes

Cooking Time: 5 minutes

Servings: 4

Ingredients:

- Buckwheat (broken) 100 g
- Turmeric powder 2 tsp
- 1 Avocado
- Tomatoes 130 g
- Tropea red onions 40 g
- Medjoul dates (pitted) 50 g
- Parsley 50 g
- Strawberries 200 g
- 2 tablespoons extra virgin olive oil
- 1 Lemon juice
- Rocket 50 g

Directions:

1. Heat up the water to cook the buckwheat.
2. When it boils, add turmeric and buckwheat. Be careful not to overcook it. It is good to leave, it "al dente." When cooked, drain the buckwheat and set aside to cool. Take a large bowl to spice the tabbouleh.

3. Cut the tomatoes into cubes and let them drain for a few minutes in a colander to remove the water.

4. On a cutting board, begin to finely chop the red onion, dates, and parsley and combine them with buckwheat.

5. Peel the avocado and cut it into small cubes and add it with the tomatoes to the buckwheat. Cut the strawberries into slices and gently add them to the rest of the ingredients. Add the chopped arugula, oil, and lemon juice. Mix all the ingredients and let the buckwheat tabbouleh take on extra flavor for an hour before serving it at the table.

Nutrients: 233: calories Fat: 4.8 g Carbohydrates 44.8 g Protein 6.9 g Sodium 17 mg

Baked Cod Marinated In Miso with Sautéed Vegetables and Sesame

Preparation Time: 8 minutes

Cooking Time: 10 minutes

Servings: 2

Ingredients:

- 300-400g of fish fillets (Mackerel, Cod, etc.)
- 2 spoons of miso
- Vegetables
- Sesame

Directions:

1. Clean the fish fillets, rinse them and dry them well with kitchen paper and mix all the seasonings in a bowl. Spread the sauce on the fish fillets, put them in a plastic bag with zipping (food use) then leave them to marinate in the fridge overnight. To cook them, take the fish fillets from the bag, remove the sauce from the fillets using kitchen paper (because this sauce burns easily during cooking)

2. The fish fillet can be roasted in the oven or fried in a pan with a little olive oil.

3. In the case of the oven: grease the grill and arrange the fillets putting the side with the skin down, cook them at 200 ° C for about 8-10 minutes, then turn them and continue to roast for 8-10 minutes

4. In the case of the pan: spread a piece of parchment paper on the pan and arrange the fillets placing the side with the skin down. Cook them on medium heat for 3-4 minutes. After that, turn the fillets and cook over low heat together with the vegetables and sesame with lid for about 10 minutes.

Nutrition: Calories: 287 Fat: 3.7 g Carbohydrates 27.9 g Protein: 24.7 g Cholesterol: 47 mg Sodium: 613 mg

Soba in a Miso Broth with Tofu, Celery, and Kale

Preparation Time: 10 minutes

Cooking Time: 20 minutes

Servings: 4

Ingredients:

- 1 l of water

- 4 teaspoons of miso paste

- Noodles 160 g

- Celery stalk and leaves 100 g

- Tofu

- Kale

- Salt

- Pepper

Directions:

1. To prepare the noodles soup, start cutting all the ingredients: then mix and cook the vegetables for about 15 minutes. Then add the water flush. Salt and pepper to taste, then to flavor the soup, grate the fresh ginger and cover with a lid to cook the soup over moderate heat for at least 20 minutes, stirring occasionally and adding more water if necessary (you will need to keep the liquid level just above the ingredients). After the

necessary time, pour the noodles into the soup and cook for a few minutes (or for the time indicated on the package).

2. At this point, also add the miso paste previously diluted in a couple of spoonsful of warm water, but be careful not to boil the broth because the nutritional properties of the miso are altered.

Nutrition: Calories: 244 Fat: 11.3g Sodium: 1549mg Potassium: 501mg Carbohydrates: 27.7g Protein: 11.9g

Lentils, Red Onion and Tomatoes Salad

Preparation Time: 20 minutes

Cooking Time: 0 minute

Servings: 3

Ingredients:

- Dried lentils 250 g
- Cherry tomatoes 10
- Fresh spring onion 1
- Chopped chives 2 tbsp.
- Chili pepper 1
- Basil 12 leaves
- Extra virgin olive oil 6 tbsp.
- White pepper to taste
- Salt to taste

Directions:

1. Boil the lentils in abundant salted water for about 20 minutes and turn off the heat when they are still crisp; if you want to soak the lentils the night before, the cooking time will be reduced by a few minutes. Drain the cooked lentils, and let them cool.

2. In the meantime, peel and finely chop the spring onion, chop the chives, cut the chili into small wheels and the

cherry tomatoes into quarters, or into even smaller pieces. In a small bowl, create an emulsion with the oil, ground pepper, and salt.

3. Place the cold lentils in a large bowl: add the previously prepared ingredients, add the chili pepper, and the basil leaves chopped with your fingers (keep a few whole to garnish the lentil salad). Season with the oil emulsion and mix everything well, adjusting if necessary, with salt. Serve after decorating the lentil salad with a few fresh basil leaves.

Nutrition: Calories: 169 Fat: 2g

Miso Caramelized Tofu

Preparation Time: 10 minutes

Cooking Time: 28 minutes

Servings: 3

Ingredients:

- 1 tbsp mirin
- 20g miso paste
- 1 * 150g firm tofu
- 40g celery, trimmed
- 35g red onion
- 120g courgette
- 1 bird's eye chili
- 1 garlic clove, finely chopped
- 1 tsp finely chopped fresh ginger
- 50g kale, chopped
- 2 tsp sesame seeds
- 35g buckwheat
- 1 tsp ground turmeric
- 2 tsp extra virgin olive oil
- 1 tsp tamari (or soy sauce)

Directions:

1. Pre-heat your over to 200C or gas mark 6. Cover a tray with baking parchment.

2. Combine the mirin and miso together. Dice the tofu and coat it in the mirin-miso mixture in a reseal able plastic bag. Set aside to marinate.

3. Chop the vegetables (except for the kale) at a diagonal angle to produce long slices. Using a steamer, cook for the kale for 5 minutes and set aside.

4. Disperse the tofu across the lined tray and garnish with sesame seeds. Roast for 20 minutes, or until caramelized.

5. Rinse the buckwheat using running water and a sieve. Add to a pan of boiling water alongside turmeric and cook the buckwheat according to the packet instructions.

6. Heat the oil in a skillet over high heat. Toss in the vegetables, herbs and spices then fry for 2-3 minutes. Reduce to a medium heat and fry for a further 5 minutes or until cooked but still crunchy.

Nutrition: Calories: 165 Carbohydrates: 15g Fat: 8g Protein: 10g

Sirtfood Cauliflower Couscous & Turkey Steak

Preparation Time: 10 minutes

Cooking Time: 10 minutes

Servings: 3

Ingredients:

- 150g cauliflower, roughly chopped
- 1 garlic clove, finely chopped
- 40g red onion, finely chopped
- 1 bird's eye chili, finely chopped
- 1 tsp finely chopped fresh ginger
- 2 tbsp. extra virgin olive oil
- 2 tsp ground turmeric
- 30g sun dried tomatoes, finely chopped
- 10g parsley
- 150g turkey steak
- 1 tsp dried sage
- Juice of ½ lemon
- 1 tbsp. capers

Directions:

1. Disintegrate the cauliflower using a food processor. Blend in 1-2 pulses until the cauliflower has a breadcrumb-like consistency.

2. In a skillet, fry garlic, chili, ginger and red onion in 1 tsp olive oil for 2-3 minutes. Throw in the turmeric and cauliflower then cook for another 1-2 minutes. Remove from heat and add the tomatoes and roughly half the parsley.

3. Garnish the turkey steak with sage and dress with oil. In a skillet, over medium heat, fry the turkey steak for 5 minutes, turning occasionally. Once the steak is cooked add lemon juice, capers and a dash of water. Stir and serve with the couscous.

Nutrition: Calories 280 Fat 17g Cholesterol 65mg Sodium 640mg Total Carbohydrate 9g Protein 26g

Red Onion Dhal

Preparation Time: 10 minutes

Cooking Time: 35 minutes

Servings: 1

Ingredients:

- 1 tsp extra virgin olive oil
- 1 tsp mustard seeds
- 40g red onion, finely chopped
- 1 garlic clove, finely chopped
- 1 tsp finely chopped fresh ginger
- 1 bird's eye chili, finely chopped
- 1 tsp mild curry powder
- 2 tsp ground turmeric
- 300ml vegetable stock
- 40g red lentils, rinsed
- 50g kale
- 50ml tinned coconut milk
- 50g buckwheat

Directions:

1. In a moderately sized sauce pan, warm the olive oil over a medium heat. Toss in the mustard seeds and fry until

they start to crackle. Add the garlic, ginger, chili and onion frying for 10 minutes, or until the onion is tender.

2. Throw in 1 tsp turmeric and curry powder, and then stir. Cook for a few minutes until fragrant, then pour in the stock and bring to the boil. Pour in the lentils and cook for 30 minutes.

3. Add the coconut milk and kale, cooking for another 5 minutes or so. As the dhal is brewing, rinse the buckwheat with water and cook it according to packet instructions. Drain and serve with the dhal.

Nutrition: Calories 40 Fat 0.1 g Cholesterol 0 mg Sodium 4 mg Potassium 146 mg Total Carbohydrate 9 g Protein 1.1 g

Tofu & Shiitake Mushroom Soup

Preparation Time: 5 minutes

Cooking Time: 13 minutes

Servings: 2

Ingredients:

- 10g dried wakame
- 1L vegetable stock
- 200g shiitake mushrooms, sliced
- 120g miso paste
- 1* 400g firm tofu, diced
- 2 green onion, trimmed and diagonally chopped
- 1 bird's eye chili, finely chopped

Directions:

1. Soak the wakame in lukewarm water for 10-15 minutes before draining.

2. In a medium-sized saucepan add the vegetable stock and bring to the boil. Toss in the mushrooms and simmer for 2-3 minutes.

3. Mix miso paste with 3-4 tbsp of vegetable stock from the saucepan, until the miso is entirely dissolved. Pour the miso-stock back into the pan and add the tofu,

wakame, green onions and chili, then serve immediately.

Nutrition: Calories 34 Fat 0.5 g Sodium 9 mg Potassium 304 mg Carbohydrate 7 g Protein 2.2 g

SIRTFOOD DINNER

Tofu & Shiitake Mushroom Soup

Preparation Time: 10 minutes

Cooking Time: 18 minutes

Servings: 3

Ingredients:

- 10g dried wakame
- 1L vegetable stock
- 200g shiitake mushrooms, sliced
- 120g miso paste
- 1* 400g firm tofu, diced
- 2 green onion, trimmed and diagonally chopped
- 1 bird's eye chili, finely chopped

Directions:

1. Soak the wakame in lukewarm water for 10-15 minutes before draining.

2. In a medium-sized saucepan add the vegetable stock and bring to the boil. Toss in the mushrooms and simmer for 2-3 minutes.

3. Mix miso paste with 3-4 tbsp of vegetable stock from the saucepan, until the miso is entirely dissolved. Pour the miso-stock back into the pan and add the tofu,

wakame, green onions and chili, then serve immediately.

Nutrition: Calories: 137.4 Carbohydrate: 11.5 g Fat: 6.7 g Protein: 9.9 g

Honey Chili Nuts

Preparation Time: 10 Minutes

Cooking Time: 30 Minutes

Servings: 4

Ingredients:

- 150g 5oz walnuts

- 150g 5oz pecan nuts

- 50g 2oz softened butter

- 1 tablespoon honey

- ½ bird's-eye chili, very finely chopped and de-seeded

- 126 calories per serving

Directions:

1. Preheat the oven to 180C/360F. Combine the butter, honey and chili in a bowl then add the nuts and stir them well. Spread the nuts onto a lined baking sheet and roast them in the oven for 10 minutes, stirring once halfway through. Remove from the oven and allow them to cool before eating.

Nutrition: Calories: 561 Fat: 412 Fat: 45.7g Salt: 279mg Carbohydrate: 23.7g Sugars: 14.18g

Pomegranate Guacamole

Preparation time: 10 Minutes

Cooking Time: 40 Minutes

Servings: 4

Ingredients:

- Flesh of 2 ripe avocados
- Seeds from 1 pomegranate
- 1 bird's-eye chili pepper, finely chopped
- ½ red onion, finely chopped
- Juice of 1 lime
- 151 calories per serving

Directions:

1. Place the avocado, onion, chill and lime juice into a blender and process until smooth. Stir in the pomegranate seeds. Chill before serving. Serve as a dip for chop vegetables.

Nutrition: Calories: 120 Fat 9g Sodium: 199mg Potassium: 357mg Carbohydrates: 8g Fiber: 5g Sugar: 2g

Chicken Curry with Potatoes and Kale

Preparation Time: 10 minutes

Cooking Time: 20 minutes

Serving: 4

- 600g chicken breast, cut into pieces
- 4 tablespoons of extra virgin olive oil
- 3 tablespoons turmeric
- 2 red onions, sliced
- 2 red chilies, finely chopped
- 3 cloves of garlic, finely chopped
- 1 tablespoon freshly chopped ginger
- 1 tablespoon curry powder
- 1 tin of small tomatoes (400ml)
- 500ml chicken broth
- 200ml coconut milk
- 2 pieces cardamom
- 1 cinnamon stick
- 600g potatoes mainly waxy
- 10g parsley, chopped
- 175g kale, chopped
- 5g coriander, chopped

Directions:

1. Marinate the chicken in a teaspoon of olive oil and a tablespoon of turmeric for about 30 minutes. Then fry in a high frying pan at high heat for about 4 minutes. Remove from the pan and set aside.

2. Heat a tablespoon of oil in a pan with chili, garlic, onion and ginger. Boil everything over medium heat and then add the curry powder and a tablespoon of turmeric and cook for another two minutes, stirring occasionally. Add tomatoes, cook for another two minutes until finally chicken stock, coconut milk, cardamom and cinnamon stick are added. Cook for about 45 to 60 minutes and add some broth if necessary.

3. In the meantime, preheat the oven to 425 °. Peel and chop the potatoes. Bring water to the boil, add the potatoes with turmeric and cook for 5 minutes. Then pour off the water and let it evaporate for about 10 minutes. Spread olive oil together with the potatoes on a baking tray and bake in the oven for 30 minutes.

4. When the potatoes and curry are almost ready, add the coriander, kale and chicken and cook for five minutes until the chicken is hot.

5. Add parsley to the potatoes and serve with the chicken curry.

Nutrition: Calories: 269.5 Fat: 6.3 g Sodium: 514.4 mg Potassium: 682.4 mg Carbohydrate: 48.5 g Protein: 7.9 g

Tofu and Curry

Preparation time: 10 Minutes

Cooking Time: 40 Minutes

Servings: 4

Ingredients:

- 8 oz. dried lentils red preferably
- 1 cup boiling water
- 1 cup frozen edamame soybeans
- 7 oz. 1/2 of most packages firm tofu, chopped into cubes
- 2 tomatoes, chopped
- 1 lime juices
- 5-6 kale leaves, stalks removed and torn
- 1 large onion, chopped
- 4 cloves garlic, peeled and grated
- 1 large chunk of ginger, grated
- 1/2 red chili pepper, deseeded use less if too much
- 1/2 tsp ground turmeric
- 1/4 tsp cayenne pepper
- 1 tsp paprika
- 1/2 tsp ground cumin

- 1 tsp salt
- 1 tbsp. olive oil

Directions:

1. Add the onion, sauté in the oil for few minutes then add the chili, garlic and ginger for a bit longer until wilted but not burned. Add the seasonings, then the lentils and stir. Add in the boiling water and cook for 10 minutes. Simmer for up to 30 minutes longer, so it will be stew-like but not overly mushy. You should check the texture of the lentils half way though.

2. Add tomato, tofu and edamame, then lime juice and kale. Test for when the kale is tender and then it is ready to serve.

Nutrition: Calories: 346.3 Fat: 26.4 g Protein: 19.1 g Saturated Fat: 2.0 g

Garbanzo Kale Curry

Preparation Time: 10 Minutes

Cooking Time: 45 Minutes

Servings: 8

Ingredients:

- 4 cups dry garbanzo beans
- Curry Paste, but go low on the heat
- 1 cup sliced tomato
- 2 cups kale leaves
- 1/2 cup coconut milk

Directions:

1. Put ingredients in the slow cooker. Cover, & cook on low for 7 to 9 hours.

Nutrition: Calories: 409 Fat: 15g Protein: 15g Carbohydrates: 53g Fiber: 11g

Kale & Shiitake Stew

Preparation Time: 10 minutes

Cooking Time: 40 minutes

Servings: 8

Ingredients:

- 3 garlic cloves, minced
- 2 cups chopped onions
- 1/2 cup olive oil
- Salt & 1 Tsp. ground pepper to taste
- 4 cups vegetable broth
- 2 pounds dry shiitake mushrooms

Directions:

1. Put ingredients in the slow cooker. Cover, & cook on low for 3 to 4 hours.

Nutrition: Calories: 285.4 Fat: 2.6 g Sodium: 358.6 mg Potassium: 1,191.3 mg Carbohydrate: 40.2 g Protein: 14.7 g

Kale & Chicken Stew

Preparation Time: 5 Minutes

Cooking Time: 55 Minutes

Servings: 4

Ingredients:

- 1 cup sliced leeks

- 1 sliced carrot

- 1 cup chopped onions

- Salt & 1 Tsp. ground pepper to taste

- 2 cups chicken broth

- 3 cups kale

- 4 pounds chicken

Directions:

1. Put ingredients in the slow cooker. Cover, & cook on low for 7 to 9 hours.

Nutrition: Calories: 293 Fat: 2.4 g Cholesterol: 15.5 mg Sodium: 1mg Carbohydrates: 53 g Protein: 17.4 g

Mushroom & Tofu Scramble

Preparation Time: 5 Minutes

Cooking Time: 35 Minutes

Servings: 1

Ingredients:

- 100g tofu, extra firm
- 1 tsp ground turmeric
- 1 tsp mild curry powder
- 20g kale, roughly chopped
- 1 tsp extra virgin olive oil
- 20g red onion, thinly sliced
- 50g mushrooms, thinly sliced
- 5g parsley, finely chopped

Directions:

1. Place 2 sheets of kitchen towel under and on-top of the tofu, then rest a considerable weight such as saucepan onto the tofu, to ensure it drains off the liquid.

2. Combine the curry powder, turmeric and 1-2 tsp of water to form a paste. Using a steamer cook kale for 3-4 minutes.

3. In a skillet, warm oil over a medium heat. Add the chili, mushrooms and onion, cooking for several minutes or until brown and tender.

4. Break the tofu in to small pieces and toss in the skillet. Coat with the spice paste and stir, ensuring everything becomes evenly coated. Cook for up to 5 minutes, or until the tofu has browned then add the kale and fry for 2 more minutes. Garnish with parsley before serving.

Nutrition: Calories: 171.8 Protein: 11.4 g; Carbohydrates: 5.4 g Sodium: 236.9 mg

SIRTFOOD VEGETABLES

Brussel Sprouts Croquettes

Preparation Time: 10 minutes

Cooking time: 25 minutes

Servings:6

Ingredients:

- 2 eggs, beaten
- 1/3 cup coconut flour
- 1 tablespoon flax meal
- ½ teaspoon salt
- ¾ cup fresh parsley, chopped
- ½ teaspoon ground black pepper
- 1 cup Brussel sprouts
- 2 eggs, whisked
- 1 tablespoon olive oil
- 2 cups water, for cooking

Directions:

1. Pour water in the pan. Add Brussel sprouts and close the lid.
2. Boil the vegetables for 15 minutes over the medium heat.
3. After this, drain water and transfer Brussel sprouts in the blender.

4. Blend the vegetables until you get smooth mass.

5. After this, transfer Brussel sprout mass in the mixing bowl.

6. Add coconut flour, flax meal salt, chopped parsley, ground black pepper, eggs, and stir with the help of the spoon until homogenous.

7. Pour olive oil in the skillet and preheat it.

8. Make the medium size croquettes from the vegetable mixture and cook them in the hot oil until golden brown.

9. Chill the croquettes little and transfer in the plates.

Nutrition: calories 87, fat 5.4, fiber 3.9, carbs 6.4, protein 4.2

Vegetable Puree

Preparation Time: 10 minutes

Cooking time: 20 minutes

Servings:3

Ingredients:

- 5 oz celery root, peeled
- 1 bell pepper
- 1 garlic clove, peeled
- 1 teaspoon avocado oil
- ¼ teaspoon salt
- 1 teaspoon butter
- 1 cup water, for cooking

Directions:

1. Remove the seeds from the bell pepper.
2. Place the celery root in the pan, add water and bring it to boil.
3. Boil the celery root for 15 minutes.
4. Then add bell pepper and switch off the heat.
5. Leave the vegetables for 2 minutes more in the hot water.
6. After this, drain the water.
7. Add garlic, avocado oil, salt, and butter.

8. Use the hand blender to blend the vegetables into a puree.

9. The cooked puree will have a soft and smooth texture.

Nutrition: calories 47, fat 1.7, fiber 1.5, carbs 7.8, protein 1.2

Curry Cauliflower Florets

Preparation Time: 10 minutes

Cooking time: 30 minutes

Servings:4

Ingredients:

- 2 cups cauliflower florets
- 1 tablespoon curry paste
- ½ cup of coconut milk
- 1 egg, whisked
- 1 cup coconut flakes

Directions:

1. Mix up together, whisk egg, curry paste, and coconut milk.
2. Then dip the cauliflower florets in the liquid and stir well.
3. Coat every cauliflower floret in the coconut flakes and transfer in the tray.
4. Preheat the oven to 360F.
5. Place the tray with the cauliflower florets in the oven and bake them for 30 minutes.
6. Flip the florets onto another side after 15 minutes of cooking.

Nutrition: calories 193, fat 17.2, fiber 3.7, carbs 8.5, protein 3.9

Marinated Green Beans

Preparation Time: 20 minutes

Cooking time: 5 minutes

Servings:4

Ingredients:

- 2 cups green beans
- 1 teaspoon chili flakes
- 3 tablespoons lemon juice
- ¼ teaspoon salt
- ½ teaspoon minced garlic
- 1 tablespoon olive oil
- ¼ red onion, diced
- 2 cups water, for cooking

Directions:

1. Pour water in the pan and bring it to boil.
2. Add green beans and boil them for 4 minutes.
3. Then drain the hot water immediately and add ice. It will save the saturated green color of the beans.
4. While the green beans are chilling, make the marinade.
5. In the shallow bowl, mix up together chili flakes, lemon juice, salt, minced garlic, and olive oil.

6. Remove the green beans from ice and place in the big bowl.

7. Sprinkle the vegetables with the marinade and add diced onion.

8. Shake the green beans well and let them marinate for 20 minutes.

Nutrition: calories 53, fat 3.7, fiber 2.1, carbs 4.9, protein 1.2

SIRTFOOD SNACK RECIPES

Strawberry Fields Salad

Preparation Time: 10 minutes

Cooking Time: 0 minute

Servings: 1

Ingredients:

- ½ cup cooked buckwheat
- 1 avocado, pitted, sliced and scooped
- 1 small tomato, quartered
- 2 Medjool dates, pitted
- 5 walnuts, chopped coarsely
- 20 g red onion
- 1 tbsp. capers
- 1 cup arugula
- 1 cup spinach
- 3 sprigs parsley, chopped
- 6 strawberries, sliced
- 1 tbsp. extra virgin olive oil
- ½ lemon, juiced
- 1 tbsp. ground turmeric

Directions:

1. Use room temperature buckwheat, or serve warm if preferred. Wash, dry and chop ingredients above, finish with the lemon and olive oil and turmeric as a dressing.

2. Add the buckwheat then the strawberries to the top of the salad.

Nutrition: Calories: 460 Fat: 26g Cholesterol: 10mg Sodium: 580mg Carbohydrates: 50g Protein: 6g

Pumpkin Brownies

Preparation Time: 10 minutes

Cooking Time: 30 minutes

Servings: 4

Ingredients:

- ¾ cup almond flour
- ½ tsp baking powder
- ½ tsp salt
- ¾ cup of coconut oil, melted
- 1 cups raw honey
- 2 tsp ground vanilla bean
- 3 eggs
- 1 tsp of cocoa powder
- 1 cup pumpkin puree
- ½ cup chopped pecans
- ¾ tsp ground cinnamon
- ½ tsp ground cloves
- ½ tsp ground nutmeg
- Sprinkle with crushed pumpkin and sunflower seeds and hemp hearts

Directions:

1. Preheat oven to 350F and grease a baking pan.

2. Mix the almond flour, baking powder, and salt together in a bowl.

3. In another bowl, mix together the melted coconut oil, honey, and vanilla bean.

4. Beat in the eggs one at a time.

5. Slowly add the flour mixture and stir.

6. Add cocoa powder, pumpkin puree, pecans, cinnamon, cloves, and nutmeg.

7. Spread the batter into the bottom of the baking pan.

8. Bake until a toothpick inserted comes out clean, 45-50 minutes.

9. Cool in the pan, cut and serve.

Nutrition: Calories: 135.3 Total Fat: 2.7 g Sugars: 14.3 g Saturated Fat: 0.8 g

Vegan Sesame Seeds Cookies

Preparation Time: 10 minutes

Cooking Time: 25 minutes

Servings: 4

Ingredients:

- 1 cup toasted sesame seeds
- 2/3 cup almond flour
- ¼ cup raw honey
- 1/8 tsp baking powder
- ¼ cup of coconut oil (or tahini)
- ¼ cup of water
- 1 tbsp lemon juice
- ¼ tsp ground vanilla bean

Directions:

1. Heat oven to 350F.
2. Blend all ingredients until you get a sticky ball.
3. Make cookies and put them on the baking tray.
4. Bake for 20 minutes at 330F, until the cookies turn slightly brown.
5. Take them out and cool.

Nutrition: Calories 42.9 Fat 2.2g

Coconut Cream Tart

Preparation Time: 10 minutes

Cooking Time: 30 minutes

Servings: 4

Ingredients:

Crust:

- 2 cups almonds, soaked overnight and drained
- 1 cup pitted dates, soaked overnight and drained
- 1 cup chopped dried apricots
- 1½ tsp ground vanilla bean
- 1 banana

Filling:

- 1 cup of flaked coconut
- 1 can of unsweetened coconut milk
- ¾ cup of raw honey
- 3 egg yolks
- 2 tbsp of arrowroot powder
- 2 tbsp of coconut oil
- 2 tsp of ground vanilla bean
- 1/8 tsp of salt
- ½ cup of coconut cream

Directions:

1. Heat the coconut milk, honey, salt and ground vanilla bean over medium heat in a medium-size saucepan.
2. In a separate bowl, whisk the egg yolks and arrowroot powder.
3. Add ½ cup of the warm coconut milk mixture to the egg yolks while whisking constantly.
4. Then pour the egg mixture back into the coconut milk mixture and whisk until the mix thickens and then mix for 3 more minutes.
5. Take off of the heat and mix in the coconut oil and flaked coconut.
6. Cool and pour in the tart crust and refrigerate.
7. Decorate with large coconut flakes.

Nutrition: Calories: 143 Total fat: 12.3g Cholesterol: 26mg Sodium: 123mg Potassium: 50mg Carbohydrates: 24.9g Fiber: 0.6g Protein: 2.6g

Oatmeal Raisin Cookies

Preparation Time: 10 minutes

Cooking Time: 25 minutes

Servings: 4

Ingredients:

- 1 cup of coconut oil
- 1 cup of coconut sugar or raw honey
- 1½ cups almond flour
- 1 tsp salt
- ½ tsp grated nutmeg
- 1 tsp cinnamon
- 1½ cups raisins
- 2 large eggs, well beaten
- 1 tbsp. ground vanilla bean
- 3 cups rolled oats
- ½ cup chopped walnuts

Directions:

1. Heat oven to 350F.
2. Grease cookie sheets with coconut oil or line with waxed or parchment paper.
3. Mix coconut oil, coconut sugar or raw honey in a large bowl and beat until fluffy.

4. Add vanilla.

5. Beat in eggs.

6. Mix almond flour, salt, cinnamon, and nutmeg in a separate bowl.

7. Stir these dry ingredients into a fluffy mixture.

8. Mix in raisins and nuts.

9. Mix in oats.

10. Spoon out on cookie sheets, leaving 2-inches between cookies.

11. Bake until edges turn golden brown.

Nutrition: Calories 100 Total Fat 2.4 g Cholesterol 16.5 mg Sodium 73.5 mg Total Carbohydrate 18.8 g Dietary Fiber 1.5 g

Vegan Superfoods Granola

Preparation Time: 10 minutes

Cooking Time: 15 minutes

Servings: 4

Ingredients:

- 10 cup rolled oats
- ½ pound shredded coconut
- 2 cup raw sunflower seeds
- 1 cup sesame seeds or chia seeds
- 3 cup chopped nuts
- 1½ cup of water
- 1½ cup of coconut oil
- 1 cup raw honey
- 1½ tsp salt
- 2 tsp cinnamon
- 1 tbsp. of ground vanilla bean
- Dried cranberries

Directions:

1. Turn the oven on and heat oven to 300F.
2. Combine water, oil, raw honey, salt, cinnamon and vanilla in a large pan.
3. Heat until raw honey is dissolved, but don't boil.

4. Pour the honey over the dry ingredients and stir well.

5. Spread onto cookie sheets.

6. Bake 25-30 minutes, and stir occasionally.

7. Let it cool.

8. Store in a cool, dry place.

Nutrition: Calories: 216.6 Total Fat: 4.6 g Sodium : 352.7 mg Potassium: 271.8 mg Carbohydrate: 42.2 g Protein: 4.5 g

Vegan Chocolate Beet Brownie

Preparation Time: 10 minutes

Cooking Time: 35 minutes

Servings: 4

Ingredients:

- 2 tbsp. chia seeds
- 1¾ cups almond flour
- ¼ tsp baking soda
- 7 tbsp. cocoa powder
- 4 ounces dark chocolate, chopped
- 1 tsp coffee
- ¾ tsp salt
- ¼ cup boiling water
- 1½ cups raw honey
- 6 tbsp. coconut oil
- 1½ tsp ground vanilla bean
- ½ cup pecans, chopped
- ½ cup beet pulp – left over after juicing

Directions:

1. Preheat your oven to 350F.
2. Line a baking dish with parchment paper.
3. Mix together the almond flour and baking soda.

4. In another bowl mix the cocoa powder, chia seeds, chocolate, coffee and salt.

5. Add the boiling water and mix.

6. Add the honey, coconut oil, vanilla and flax meal mixture and blend.

7. Stir in the pecans and beet pulp.

8. Put the mix to a baking dish and bake.

9. Let cool and serve.

Nutrition: Calories 96 Total Fat 3.4 g Sodium 109.7 mg Carbohydrate 19.2 Dietary Fiber 1.6 g

Vegan Cacao Chia Cookies

Preparation Time: 10 minutes

Cooking Time: 35 minutes

Servings: 4

Ingredients:

- 4 tbsp of raw cacao powder
- 3 tbsp of chia seeds
- 1 cup of almonds
- 1 cup of cashews
- 1 cup of buckwheat flour
- 2 tbsp of coconut oil
- 1/3 of a cup of raw honey
- ¼ of a cup of dates
- ¼ of a cup of water

Directions:

1. Heat oven to 350F.
2. Blend all ingredients until you get a sticky ball.
3. Make cookies and put them on the baking tray.
4. Bake for 20 minutes at 350F, until the cookies turn slightly brown.
5. Take them out and cool.

Nutrition: Calories 96 Total Fat 3.4 g Sodium 109.7 mg Carbohydrate 19.2 Dietary Fiber 1.6 g

Sweet Superfoods Pie Crust

Preparation Time: 10 minutes

Cooking Time: 30 minutes

Servings: 4

Ingredients:

- 1 1/3 cups blanched almond flour
- 1/3 cup tapioca flour
- ½ tsp sea salt
- 1 large egg
- ¼ cup of coconut oil
- 2 tbsp. coconut sugar or raw honey
- 1 tsp of ground vanilla bean

Directions:

1. Place almond flour, tapioca flour, sea salt, vanilla, egg and coconut sugar (if you use coconut sugar) in the bowl of a food processor.
2. Process 2-3 times to combine.
3. Add oil and sugar (or raw honey) and pulse with several one-second pulses and then let the food processor run until the mixture comes together.
4. Pour dough onto a sheet of plastic wrap.
5. Wrap and then press the dough into a 9-inch disk.

6. Refrigerate for 30 minutes.

Nutrition: Calories 527 Total Fat 35 g Cholesterol 0 mg Sodium 542 mg Potassium 67 mg Carbohydrate 48 g Protein 6 g

Apple Pie

Preparation Time: 10 minutes

Cooking Time: 35 minutes

Servings: 4

Ingredients:

- For the crust:
- See the previous recipe
- For the apple filling:
- 2 tbsp coconut oil
- 9 sour apples, peeled, cored and cut into ¼-inch thick slices
- ¼ cup of coconut sugar or raw honey
- ½ tsp cinnamon
- 1/8 tsp sea salt
- ½ cup of coconut milk
- For the topping:
- 1 cup ground nuts and seeds

Directions:

1. Filling: melt coconut oil in a large pot over medium heat.
2. Add apples, coconut sugar or raw honey, cinnamon and sea salt.

3. Increase heat to medium-high and cook, occasionally stirring, until apples release their moisture and sugar is melted.
4. Pour coconut milk or cream over apples and continue to cook until apples are soft and liquid has thickened, about 5 minutes, stirring occasionally.
5. Pour the filling into the crust and then top with topping.
6. Place a pie shield over the edges of the crust to avoid burning.
7. Bake until topping is just turning golden brown.
8. Cool and serve.

Nutrition: Calories 237 Total Fat 11 g Cholesterol 0 mg Sodium 266 mg Potassium 65 mg Carbohydrate 34 g Protein 1.9 g

Sirtfood Juices and Smoothies

Creamy Strawberry & Cherry Smoothie

Preparation Time: 7 minutes

Cooking Time: 0 minute

Servings: 1

Ingredients:

- 100g (3½ oz) strawberries

- 75g (3oz) frozen pitted cherries

- 1 tablespoon plain full-fat yogurt

- 175mls (6fl oz) unsweetened soya milk

Directions:

1. Place all of the ingredients into a blender and process until smooth. Serve and enjoy.

Nutrition: Calories: 132

Grape, Celery & Parsley Reviver

Preparation Time: 7 minutes

Cooking Time: 0 minute

Servings: 1

Ingredients:

- 75g (3oz) red grapes

- 3 sticks of celery

- 1 avocado, de-stoned and peeled

- 1 tablespoon fresh parsley

- ½ teaspoon matcha powder

Directions:

1. Place all of the ingredients into a blender with enough water to cover them and blitz until smooth and creamy. Add crushed ice to make it even more refreshing.

Nutrition: Calories: 334

Strawberry & Citrus Blend

Preparation Time: 5 minutes

Cooking Time: 0 minute

Servings: 1

Ingredients:

- 75g (3oz) strawberries

- 1 apple, cored

- 1 orange, peeled

- ½ avocado, peeled and de-stoned

- ½ teaspoon matcha powder

- Juice of 1 lime

Directions:

1. Place all of the ingredients into a blender with enough water to cover them and process until smooth.

Nutrition: Calories: 272

Grapefruit & Celery Blast

Preparation Time: 5 minutes

Cooking Time: 0 minute

Servings: 1

Ingredients:

- 1 grapefruit, peeled

- 2 stalks of celery

- 50g (2oz) kale

- ½ teaspoon matcha powder

Directions:

1. Place all the ingredients into a blender with enough water to cover them and blitz until smooth.

Nutrition: Calories: 71

Sirt Desserts

Orange & Celery Crush

Preparation Time: 5 minutes

Cooking Time: 0 minute

Servings: 1

Ingredients:

- 1 carrot, peeled
- 3 stalks of celery
- 1 orange, peeled
- ½ teaspoon matcha powder
- Juice of 1 lime

Directions:

1. Place all of the ingredients into a blender with enough water to cover them and blitz until smooth.

Nutrition: Calories: 95

Tropical Chocolate Delight

Preparation Time: 7 minutes

Cooking Time: 0 minute

Servings: 1

Ingredients:

- 1 mango, peeled & de-stoned
- 75g (3oz) fresh pineapple, chopped

- 50g (2oz) kale

- 25g (1oz) rocket

- 1 tablespoon 100% cocoa powder or cacao nibs

- 150mls (5fl oz) coconut milk

Directions:

1. Place all of the ingredients into a blender and blitz until smooth. You can add a little water if it seems too thick.

Nutrition: Calories: 427

Walnut & Spiced Apple Tonic

Preparation Time: 5 minutes

Cooking Time: 0 minute

Servings: 1

Ingredients:

- Ingredients

- 6 walnuts halves

- 1 apple, cored

- 1 banana

- ½ teaspoon matcha powder

- ½ teaspoon cinnamon

- Pinch of ground nutmeg

Directions:

1. Place all of the ingredients into a blender and add sufficient water to cover them. Blitz until smooth and creamy.

Nutrition: Calories: 272

Pineapple & Cucumber Smoothie

Preparation Time: 5 minutes

Cooking Time: 0 minute

Servings: 1

Ingredients:

- 50g (2oz) cucumber
- 1 stalk of celery
- 2 slices of fresh pineapple
- 2 sprigs of parsley
- ½ teaspoon matcha powder
- Squeeze of lemon juice

Directions:

1. Place all of the ingredients into blender with enough water to cover them and blitz until smooth.

Nutrition: Calories: 77

CONCLUSION

Time and time once again, I've explained to you guys the problem with the majority of diets: restrictive consuming. When it pertains to constraint, our rebel impulses desire to stick it to the guy and binge like crazy. I'm quite sure you'll also become that good friend that nobody desires to go out with because of your brand-new hangry character. For realists, there have not been sufficient constant research studies that say calorie limitation is the way to go. You'll lose some sweet however you'll also fulfill some undesirable outcomes and ultimately restore the weight. Research studies looking at caloric constraint discovered that in time limitation results in loss of muscle mass (which completely counters what the sirtfood diet plan claims it can do), muscle strength and loss of bone, anemia, depression, and irritation.

The most significant claim this diet boasts about is these sirtuin proteins increase our body's ability to burn fat, promote muscle repair work, growth and upkeep and as pointed out earlier- quick weight-loss. Right?! Because rapid weight loss is always safe. Other non-weight associated advantages consist of: improving memory, managing blood sugar level levels, and protecting you from cancers and persistent illness.

The Sirtfood diet stresses consuming foods that might engage with a household of proteins known to be as sirtuin proteins (now the name of the diet plan is starting to make sense). Since of the role they play in the metabolic process, some professionals are calling sirtuins "slim genes" for their prospective function in weight loss.

Sirtfoods promote sirtuin genes, which are stated to influence the body's capability to burn fat and boost the metabolic system.

The Sirtfood diet plan is based upon 2 stages:

Phase one is an intensive seven-day program developed to kick-start your intense weight reduction.

Then stage 2 has to do with upping the amount of Sirtfood-rich fruit and vegetables in your everyday meals to preserve weight-loss.

Unlike numerous short-term diets, the Sirtfood plan includes meals and guidance on how to keep off the weight you lose in the very first week by continuing to incorporate Sirtfoods as part of a well-balanced and healthy diet plan

CPSIA information can be obtained
at www.ICGtesting.com
Printed in the USA
BVHW010731150621
609525BV00014B/72

9 781803 254067